Wherever you wait on the platform in 1934, a vending machine is to hand!

AUTOMATIC
VENDING MACHINES

Colin Emmins

Shire Publications Ltd

CONTENTS

*Published in 1995 by Shire Publications Ltd,
Cromwell House, Church Street, Princes Ris-
borough, Buckinghamshire HP27 9AA, UK.*
Copyright © 1995 by Colin Emmins. First
published 1995. Shire Album 316. ISBN 0 7478
0287 4.

Printed in Great Britain by CIT Printing Services, Press Buildings, Merlins Bridge, Haverford-
west, Dyfed SA61 1XF.

British Library Cataloguing in Publication Data: Emmins, Colin. Automatic Vending
Machines. – (Shire Albums; No. 316). I. Title II. Series 629.82. ISBN 0-7478-0287-4.

ACKNOWLEDGEMENTS
Illustrations are acknowledged as follows: Autobar Food Services Group, front cover; Bristol
Industrial Museum, pages 2, 8 (left), 11 (all), 12 (top two), 13 (bottom); British Telecommuni-
cations plc 1992, pages 10 (bottom right), 29 (top); British Transport Museum, pages 1, 3, 8
(right), 9 (right), 10 (top), 14, 20 (bottom), 28 (top); National Railway Museum, page 9 (top
right); Penguin Books Ltd, page 13 (top); Post Office Archives and Records Centre, pages 5
(bottom), 10 (bottom left), 12 (bottom); Provend Services Ltd, page 19 (right); Salter Weigh-
Tronix Ltd, page 9 (top left); Mr George Sandy, pages 6, 7, 16 (both), 20 (top), 21 (bottom),
32; Sankey Vending, pages 18 (top), 25 (top), 27 (both); Mr Eddie Smith, page 23 (both);
Westminster City Archives, page 21 (top); Wittenborg UK Ltd, pages 15, 17, 18 (bottom), 19
(left), 31 (bottom).
    The author wishes to thank members of the Automatic Vending Association of Britain for
their freely given help in supplying information during the preparation of this book.

Cover: *Cast-iron column-and-drawer vending machine from c.1914 designed for the British
Automatic Machine Company Ltd, who owned and operated it, to sell confectionery, cigarettes
and matches.*

Below: *An outdoor four-column cigarette machine, manufactured from cast aluminium by
Brecknell Munro & Roberts Ltd of Bristol, photographed outside a shop at Bath in 1926.*

Machines selling tickets for District Line destinations and a Nestlé Penny Red chocolate-vending machine at Hammersmith underground station, London, 1923.

FORERUNNERS AND THE EARLY YEARS

Automatic vending as it is known today began in the later years of the nineteenth century, although designs for selling holy water, snuff and tobacco, books and postage stamps provide earlier examples of human ingenuity in using a coin not simply to pay for goods but to activate the equipment through which the goods are supplied.

Indeed, as early as 215 BC the mathematician Hero of Alexandria published a method of dispensing holy water through a coin-operated mechanism. The water was contained in a covered urn in which an upright rod balanced on one side a small plate, while on the other side a bell-shaped cap was suspended to fit over and close the water outlet from the urn. The position of the plate under a slit in the top of the urn ensured that when a coin was pushed through the slit it dropped on to the plate, depressing it so as to lift the cap on the other side. The outlet being thus opened, the water flowed freely until the coin slid off the tipped plate, sending the apparatus into reverse to stop the flow. How much water the Egyptian worshipper received for the money was a matter of chance and it is not known whether the device was ever put into practice. Nonetheless, it remains the first recorded example of a coin-operated vending machine.

In Britain it was not until the seven-

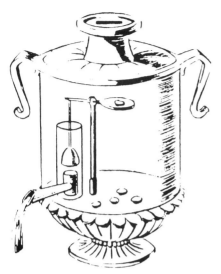

A sketch reconstruction of Hero's holy-water vender of 215 BC.

teenth century that the first instance of automatic vending was recorded. It was a device known as an honour box, for dispensing snuff or tobacco, which was used in taverns and held about 1 pound (450 grams) of tobacco or the equivalent of snuff. An old English halfpenny dropped in the slot triggered the opening of the

spring-loaded lid, but the device was less ingenious than Hero's, for unless the user closed the box by hand – as he was on his honour to do – other customers could help themselves to the contents without paying.

Customers must have been generally honest, for honour boxes continued to be used. One Victorian specimen was inscribed on the lid:

'One penny put into the till
Press down the knob and you may fill
And when you've filled without delay
Shut down the lid or sixpence pay.'

Sixpence was the fine imposed on the careless user.

Early in the nineteenth century a radical bookseller, Richard Carlile, sought to circumvent the laws against selling seditious or blasphemous books by installing a clockwork device whereby, he claimed, a buyer could turn the handle of a dial to the publication he sought, deposit the money and have the book dispensed to him automatically without a human seller. It was to no avail: no details of the device remain, but the courts still found Carlile guilty as the seller.

Later in the century automatic vending machines began to appear among the patented inventions of a busy age. Among the earliest, in 1857, was Simeon

An honour box for selling tobacco or snuff in inns and clubs.

4

Denham's 'self-acting machine' for obtaining a penny postage stamp on inserting the appropriate coin. The stamps passed in a strip between rollers and the penny piece rolled down an incline, activating certain levers within the machine so as to extrude a single stamp against a cutting edge where it could be torn off.

The machine allowed a halfpenny to fall through the apparatus and be returned without activating the mechanism. It was not until 1907 that stamp-vending machines, operating on principles similar to those of Denham's patent fifty years before, were first installed inside post offices, followed shortly afterwards by machines outside.

But it is one thing to patent an invention and quite another to put it on the market. It was Percival Everitt, a London engineer, whose interest in automatic vending caused him in the 1880s to patent and develop several devices. One of them, a machine to sell postcards and writing paper, was installed in 1883 in the street outside Mansion House underground station in the City of London.

The machine was marketed by the Post Card and Stamped Letter Public Supply Company, the first stamp-machine company to be licensed by the Post Office – with the incidental proviso that the equipment should state that the company had no connection with the Post Office!

Everitt's apparatus was activated by the weight of the coin as it rolled

Left: *Everitt's machine supplying stamped postcards in the 1880s.*

Below: *Part of an advertisement for Everitt's stamped-postcard machine, with the official patent in the centre.*

The Post Card & Stamped Letter Public Supply Co.

through a series of pivoted levers within the machine which eventually unlocked the delivery mechanism. When filled, the stack of postcards rested upon the bent, underlying end of another lever which, once the stack was exhausted, rocked back, lifting a rod which allowed a tablet marked 'Empty' at its other end to slip through a slit in the case so that it could be seen by the customer. At the same time a similar device closed the coin entry slot. Like Denham, Everitt also incorporated a bypass for smaller coins.

Everitt's subsequent patents illustrated – by their attempts to cure them – the practical problems encountered by the early inventors. In one of them he noted that his earlier machine worked well when properly used but had been abused by the insertion of 'articles such as pieces of paper, orange peel and other rubbish' – in lieu, presumably, of honest coin – which had fouled the works. The machine had also been found susceptible to manipulation so as to dispense more than one article for the money inserted.

To judge from the recurrence of improved patents, these two ways of cheating the machine, the insertion of various coin substitutes (or 'slugs' as the machine owners called them) in an effort to activate the mechanism without payment and interference with the machine once activated in order to obtain more than the strict entitlement, remained the principal drawbacks from the owner's point of view.

Other Everitt patents were a coin-operated dispenser of water and other liquids, an automatic snack-vending apparatus for the combined delivery of food and liquid, for example, biscuits and water, a coin-freed (operating only on the insertion of a coin) weighing machine, a coin-freed apparatus for hiring opera glasses and a device for dating or stamping pre-paid tickets to be dispensed from the machine.

Another inventor of the period was Frederick Charles Lynde of Manchester, whose patents included one containing a magnet to detect false coin. Other mechanical devices were introduced over the years to check for false coin by reference to its diameter, thickness, weight or surface of the rim, or even by probing it for holes. The primary check to false coin remained the size of the entry slot itself.

In time the manufacture of coin rejection equipment became a specialised section of the automatic vending industry, as it became clear that failure to activate the coin mechanism was the most likely cause of a machine not delivering the goods.

However, during the 1880s the wave of invention gave way to the practical devel-

A gravity release machine vending chocolate eggs, c.1900. A coin released the handle and the egg dropped into the bowl.

opment of existing equipment by a new industry and by the next decade London and provincial trade directories were listing automatic-delivery machine manufacture as a distinct commercial category. The titles of some of the early companies, such as the Postcard Automatic Supply Company, the Sweetmeat Automatic Delivery Company and, a little later, the International Automatic Opera Glass Box Company suggest something of the range of goods available.

The most common of all the early machines were operated on the so-called column-and-drawer principle, still known today. Goods sold in neat rectangular packs, like chocolate bars or packets of cigarettes, were stacked in a column one above the other inside the machine. A glass window down the front of the machine enabled the customer to see whether the stock had run out but was designed to be too narrow for a villain to remove the contents were he to smash the glass. A coin inserted in the slot at the top descended by gravity through the machine activating the mechanics until, its journey complete, the purchaser could pull open the drawer at the foot of the column and remove the lowest item from the column of stock. Closing the drawer relocked the system while the pressure of the remaining stock moved the next article into the drawer to await a further customer.

From the early years many machines have been dedicated to the supply of particular products and brands, with Cadbury and Nestlé well-known names on chocolate and confectionery dispensers and the brand names of the Imperial Tobacco Company on cigarette machines. Because prices were stable between the two world wars machines such as the Nestlé Penny Red chocolate vender – a red painted machine dispensing a penny chocolate bar in a red wrapper – operated profitably and successfully for many years. In the 1920s chewing gum, a product from the United States, made its first appearance in British vending machines. The name on the machine was usually Wrigley's.

From the outset vending machines were popular with travellers and soon became familiar features on railway station platforms.

Another popular piece of station furniture was the weighing machine (another Everitt patent originally) which indicated weight on a large dial. More sophisticated versions could also either issue a card with the weight printed on it or even announce it ('speak your weight').

Penny platform tickets, permitting entry to the railway station platform for those not actually travelling, were usually dispensed from machines. On the London underground, where rush-hour crowds made speed essential, travel ticket machines were introduced in 1904 and gradually spread through the network.

So automatic vending machines were supplying services as well as goods. Telephone booths, first introduced in 1925, were installed in many public places by the end of the decade. Their first coin mechanisms were also purely mechanical. The caller inserted the money, dialled

A 1920s machine for vending orange drops. It works on the gravity principle.

Passengers could buy Churchmans cigarettes, wax matches, chocolate (Nestlé included free gifts for coupons collected), Palm toffee, throat pastilles, Sun Maid raisins, Beech Nut chewing gum or check their weight while waiting for the train, 1934.

the number and was answered. He then pressed 'Button A', which deposited his money in the cash box of the machine, in order to be heard at the other end of the line. If the call failed to connect, he pressed button B and his money bypassed the cash box and fell to the bottom of the machine where it could be retrieved. The last of such booths was finally taken out of service on one of the Shetland Isles in 1994.

But the vending of goods remained at the heart of the industry, which continued to expand, not only in the number of companies making the equipment but also in the growth of firms set up to service machines throughout Britain by maintaining and refilling them and collecting the money. Vending had spread from the railway station to the high street. Machines outside many shops sold confectionery and cigarettes even when the shop itself was shut. Hotels and clubs installed cigarette machines.

Right: *An automatic personal weighing machine designed to be used inside or outside 'at places of public resort' by George Salter & Company Ltd of West Bromwich. This model was made before the First World War, taking up Everitt's patents.*

Below: *A later version of the London Underground automatic ticket machines first installed in 1908.*

Above: *A platform 'ticket issuing machine' owned by the 'GW & GC' (Great Western and Great Central Railways) and used between the two world wars, photographed in 1978 at the National Railway Museum, York. Attached to the pillar behind, and visible on either side, can be seen museum postcard machines.*

Firms like the British Automatic Company Ltd (BAC) would develop suitable machines, sell or, more usually, lease them to the retailer, and employ service engineers to maintain them thereafter. Alternatively, a machine dedicated to selling a specific brand of product might be supplied by the brand owner, who would come to an arrangement with the retailer for stocking, maintaining and emptying the machine. The stock, particularly of

By the 1930s machines giving change for 6d, 1s, 2s and 2s 6d pieces had been installed at busier stations. The stacked change can be seen through the glass panel.

Below left: *Stamp-vending machines in use outside a post office c.1910.*

Below right: *A public telephone booth with Button A and Button B equipment. Money was returned into the small cup below 'B'.*

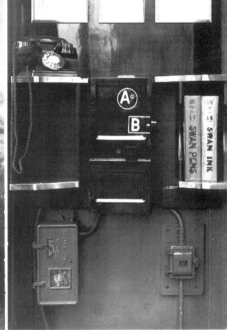

cigarettes or confectionery, was usually in the same packaging as the brand of goods within the shop.

Attempts were made to extend the range of goods sold. Penguin paperback books, themselves a popular innovation of the 1930s, were sold experimentally in machines quaintly named 'Penguincubators', which allowed the reader to choose from a wide selection all at the same price. Rolls of photographic film were marketed similarly. Experiments were made to sell petrol from automatic machines.

By the outbreak of the Second World War in 1939 most people were accustomed to using coin-operated machines and the less well-off would

Above: A 1920s confectionery and tobacconist shop with cigarette vender outside; a machine in similar style for matches is to the right of the door under the Pascall sign.

Below: Two wall-mounted cigarette machines from the 1920s. (Left) This machine sold Gold Flake and Players Navy Cut, two popular cigarette brands between the wars, at 1s for a packet of twenty. (Right) A wooden case machine selling ten Wills' Wild Woodbines for 2d.

Left: *An up-market cigarette vender pretending to be a wooden cabinet at the Grand Pump Room Hotel, Bath, in the 1920s.*

Right: *Behind the casing of a six-column cigarette vender. The coin weight enables release levers to move via a rotating rod. Removing the packet and closing the drawer allows the coin to drop into the cash box and the mechanism to move back to the original position.*

An outdoor stamp machine selling 1d and ¹/₂d stamps at a post office, 1936.

Right: *Allen Lane, the publisher of Penguin Books, demonstrates the Penguincubator in 1937. He has chosen 'Practical Economics' over the other featured covers, 'The Murders in Praed Street' and 'The Jungle'.*

Below: *An early attempt to vend petrol automatically – from the white pump on its own in the centre of the picture – photographed at Cleeve, Somerset, in 1927.*

By 1939 machine design was showing greater sophistication: an early success in harmonising the 'Auto Shop' with its surroundings. Everything from this elegant machine cost 1d.

probably be paying for domestic gas or electricity through coin-in-the-slot meters installed in the home.

But the war stopped the industry in its tracks. Vending machines were no longer produced as the factories were diverted to general engineering for war work. The available goods were sold by more traditional means.

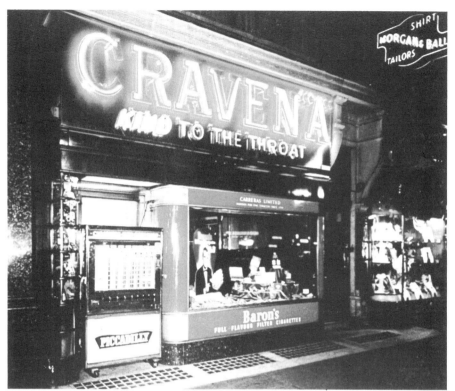

In what appears to be a special space next to Carreras, who not only sold but made cigarettes, is a postwar 'Ever open shop', showing a distinctive change of style.

MID-CENTURY DEVELOPMENTS

After the war, the first instinct of British suppliers was quickly to bring over machines from the United States, where the chief innovations in equipment were being made. However, restrictions on spending dollars imposed practical difficulties on importing from America and the British vending-machine manufacturing industry had the incentive to revive. The first post-war machines were still constructed mainly for the sale of confectionery, chewing gum and cigarettes. Pressed steel replaced the familiar cast-iron casing of many column-and-drawer machines.

However, many new machines were more versatile both in their design and in the range of goods they could offer. The drop-flap machine, for example, was a more sophisticated version of the column-and-drawer: the goods were still stacked vertically within the machine but each package rested on a small metal shelf. The insertion of the coin into the machine activated a vending cycle which dropped the hinge of the lowest shelf so that its package fell through a chute into a hopper at the foot of the machine. The customer then pushed open the transparent flap to retrieve the goods from the hopper. The open flap, unbeknown to the customer, pressed against a further mechanism within the machine to relock the system. One advantage was that the goods sold through the drop-flap did not need to be so uniformly packaged as those in the column-and-drawer. Updated versions of the system are still in use.

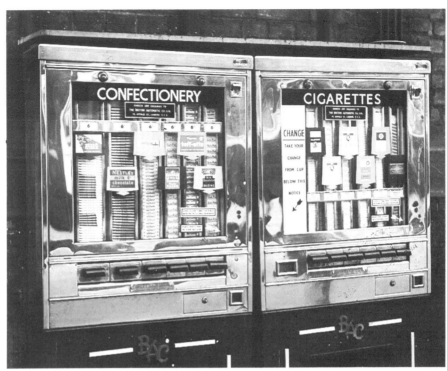

A pair of matching pressed stainless steel machines for the station platform.

An early 'auto shop' of the 1960s with packs of different shapes.

A cupboard machine with (left) a separate hot drinks and soup vender.

The compartment, or cupboard, machine came in at much the same time. The goods, all selling for the same price, were displayed in a bank of small cupboards with glass doors through which the customer could see them . After he had inserted the correct money the customer could open one cupboard and remove the contents. An interlocking mechanism ensured that only one cupboard could be opened for the coin paid. Because goods were independently accessible, a wider variety could be offered than by either the column-and-drawer or the drop-flap system,where the customer could buy only the next article in line. Cupboard machines may still be seen offering, for example, packaged snacks and filled sandwiches.

Other machines combined the display advantages of the cupboard machine with the delivery mechanism of the drop-flap to provide, in effect, an automatic shop.

Soon after the war drop-flap machines which sold just packaged milk came to the relief of customers needing a supply when shops were shut. Sales from these machines rose during the 1950s but early in the next decade inflation, a phenomenon

of little consequence earlier in the century, effectively ended the trade when the price of milk started to go up. Traditionally the size of vending packs could be modified to cope with slight price fluctuations, but in the case of milk the law decreed that it be sold in standard quantities. Machine technology did not yet allow for multi-coin vending and it was too expensive continually to modify the machines.

Milk vending, however, had introduced three new features which remained important to the wider vending industry: vended milk had been homogenised to prolong its life; it was packaged in laminated aseptic cartons and it had been kept cool by electric refrigeration. Homogenised milk was a useful ingredient in milk-based products and laminated cartons were later used for packaging soft drinks and fruit juices.

But it was the use of electricity that had the widest implications: cooler temperatures were ideal for keeping packaged milk and soft drinks in good condition; heat was essential in the development of the market for ready-to-drink hot beverages,

17

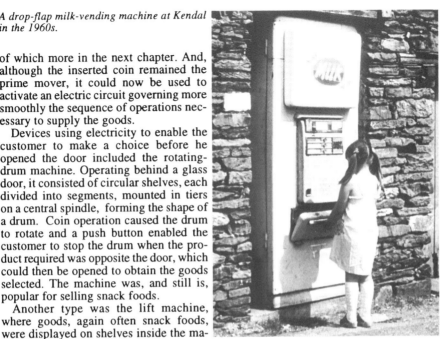

A drop-flap milk-vending machine at Kendal in the 1960s.

of which more in the next chapter. And, although the inserted coin remained the prime mover, it could now be used to activate an electric circuit governing more smoothly the sequence of operations necessary to supply the goods.

Devices using electricity to enable the customer to make a choice before he opened the door included the rotating-drum machine. Operating behind a glass door, it consisted of circular shelves, each divided into segments, mounted in tiers on a central spindle, forming the shape of a drum. Coin operation caused the drum to rotate and a push button enabled the customer to stop the drum when the product required was opposite the door, which could then be opened to obtain the goods selected. The machine was, and still is, popular for selling snack foods.

Another type was the lift machine, where goods, again often snack foods, were displayed on shelves inside the ma-

Next to the sleek 'Automat' ever-open shop stand drop-flap milk venders (right).

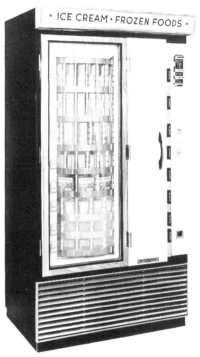

Filling a rotating-drum snack-vending machine.

A rotating-drum machine from the late 1950s, selling frozen foods.

chine. Coin operation and a panel of press buttons to select the chosen snack caused a lift to rise to the appropriate shelf and the snack to move forward on a conveyor to the lift, which then lowered it to the delivery point below.

Design engineers continued to improve on the means of displaying goods within the machines. One system provided for packs to be suspended by peg clips from a series of parallel chains, each offering a different branded package. The machine's motor, activated by the inserted coin, drove forward the chain bearing the particular package selected until the front peg of the series pressed against a rod which caused the peg to open and release the package required into the hopper below. By the late 1960s the spiral coil was preferred to the peg as a retainer since it kept the goods more reliably in place while still allowing the colourful packaging to tempt the customer. At this time basic

standard dimensions for the equipment were agreed between the manufacturers so that, for example, a bank of different machines would all be the same height.

New developments also extended coin-operated automation to a greater range of services. One example was the booth for coin-operated portrait photography. The invention of an automatic picture-taking machine had been reported as early as 1890 but it was not until the mid twentieth century that the customer was able to sit inside a photographic booth, put a coin in the slot, face the camera and obtain within minutes an inexpensive portrait photograph.

Another innovative coin-operated service sped the growth of a whole new retail sector. The Second World War had sent more and more women out to work whilst employment in domestic service had drastically declined. The launderette, with its battery of coin-operated washing machines and dryers, had been pioneered in the United States just before the war but its arrival in Britain in the late 1950s

19

Soon after, automatic equipment was installed to control larger car parks. The exact money inserted in the machine automatically lifted a barrier, allowing access to the car park. Elsewhere pay-and-display equipment automatically dispensed, on payment of the parking fee, a ticket for display on the windscreen of the parked car as proof of payment.

A late 1960s drop-flap machine, the products held by spiral coils.

A 1950s booth for automatic self-photography at Baker Street station, London.

helped women – or townswomen at least – to avoid a time-consuming domestic chore without the need either to wait for the laundry van to call or to find the capital to invest in a washing machine of their own. Soon many launderettes had also installed coin-operated drying and dry cleaning machines as a natural extension of their service.

From 1958 pre-payment parking meters appeared on the streets of London and elsewhere, each on its individual column indicating the length of time paid for parking in a single street-side car space.

One of the first sets of parking meters, installed by the City of Westminster in 1958.

An early automatic snack bar with the machines set in unifying decor, designed for use at Madame Tussauds exhibition, London.

An American machine for vending drinking water, 1908.

VENDING REFRESHMENT

The automatic vending of food – and especially snack foods and beverages – continued to increase during the 1960s. Annual sales of machines for this purpose alone doubled between 1965 and 1970, when nearly thirty thousand such machines were sold in the year. By then it was estimated that over one hundred thousand food- and drink-vending machines were in use in factories, offices and other organisations throughout Britain and vending sales of hot drinks alone – tea, coffee and chocolate – were said to be worth some £47 million.

Selling drinks automatically began a long time ago. An automatic coin-operated fountain for dispensing drinks was in commercial use in France by the 1890s and during the first half of the twentieth century Americans in particular were experimenting with beverage vending. The first American hot drinks machine using electricity to produce hot coffee appeared in the 1940s and came to Britain a decade later. Those first machines produced only hot coffee and chocolate. To become fully accepted in Britain, however, vending machines needed also to provide tea and various attempts were made to that end.

At first the ingredients of the drink were in powdered form but the powdered tea proved particularly unpalatable and a machine was next devised which used leaf tea and liquid milk. By 1970, however, spray-dried instantly soluble tea and coffee were available to meet more effectively the requirements of the equipment and the tastes of the consumer.

Disposable paper or plastic cups designed to stack inside the machine so as to make best use of the space were already available. Each cup had a lip around the rim so that it could more easily be separated from the rest when its turn came to be dispensed. For hot drinks, however, none of them was sufficiently heat-resistant and they had therefore to be adapted to the new market.

A typical coin-operated hot drinks machine would be loaded with separate containers of each of the dry ingredients and with stacked cups. When appropriate coin was inserted and a button pushed to select the drink required, a cup was released to receive it. Within the machine, hot water flowed from a tank into a mixing bowl into which the ingredients were released in pre-set proportions to be blended together. The drink was then dispensed into the waiting cup. Once the cup was filled, the sequence was complete and the liquid automatically stopped flowing. Meanwhile the hot water tank was automatically topped up and the mixing bowl washed ready for the next drink. Such systems are still in use.

Whilst the hot drinks market was being extended to include, for example, soup, a growing number of cold drinks were dispensed through other coin-operated ma-

Inside the Rank 'Teamatic', showing how the cups and fresh ingredients are stored.

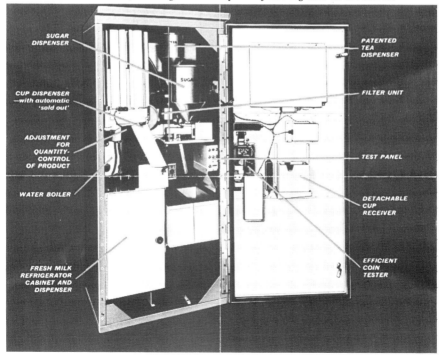

SUGAR DISPENSER

CUP DISPENSER —with automatic 'sold out'

ADJUSTMENT FOR QUANTITY-CONTROL OF PRODUCT

WATER BOILER

FRESH MILK REFRIGERATOR CABINET AND DISPENSER

PATENTED TEA DISPENSER

FILTER UNIT

TEST PANEL

DETACHABLE CUP RECEIVER

EFFICIENT COIN TESTER

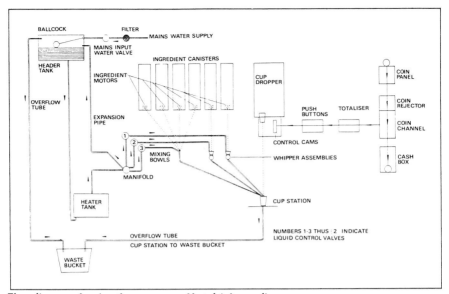

Flow diagram showing the sequence of hot drinks vending.

chines. Soft drinks for this purpose were produced in two different ways: either the pre-mix method, which made up the drink in advance in a sealed container which the vending machine had only to chill before dispensing; or post-mix, where a concentrate was mixed with water, chilled and carbonated within the machine itself, to be served when required. Other vending machines were designed to sell soft

Flow diagram showing post-mix vending of chilled carbonated soft drinks.

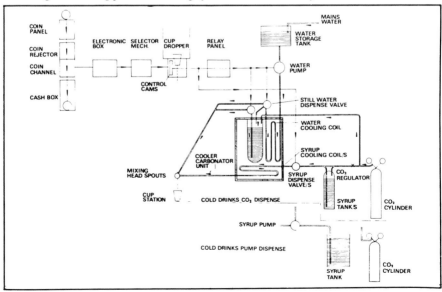

A choice of Wall's ice cream, Kia-Ora orange squash or Express Dairy milk offered in the early 1960s.

Vending chilled canned soft drinks on a service station forecourt in the 1980s.

drinks already packed in bottles. These had been pioneered in America by the giant cola corporations. Later the can replaced the glass bottle as the preferred pack for such machines.

By the late 1960s some machines were able to supply both hot and cold drinks when the buyer inserted the money and pressed the appropriate button on the display panel.

Later came the in-cup vending system, which pre-fills each cup with the dry ingredients before they are stacked and sealed for use in the machine. In the machine the cup simply requires the addition of water to dissolve the ingredients and provide the selected drink. The system is particularly attractive to manufacturers of branded products since it allows greater control over the finished beverage.

By the end of the 1960s the conventional tea-break in factories and offices was rapidly disappearing in the face of the automatic vending machine. 'Ethel with her tea trolley is the epitome of British inefficiency and we want to get rid of her right away' was the view of one management expert of the day.

Once initial consumer resistance had been overcome, the tea trolley passed from the norm to the outmoded in most workplaces within a very few years.

The conventional automatic drinks-vending machine was either free-standing or wall-mounted. As vending spread to smaller workplaces, table-top vending machines were developed.

Hot food vending was also being pioneered in the 1960s with the intention of promoting fully automated works canteens, particularly for shift and night workers, whose meals could then be prepared in advance during the conventional working day. The initial problem was how to preserve the freshly cooked food for re-heating later. The cook-chill system was adopted, in which food was preserved by blast-freezing and could be reheated in a microwave oven coin-operated by the hungry customer.

From the outset the coin-operated vending machine was only as efficient as the operator, who kept it stocked, collected and checked the cash and corrected any basic mechanical faults. Mechanical breakdown could usually be prevented by simple routine cleaning and maintenance. Electricity introduced greater sophistication into the works and design improvements grouped the more intricate sections of the equipment into removable units, any one of which could be replaced when necessary and taken back to the workshop for more extensive repairs without leaving the machine itself out of order. Another aspect of reliable service was the building in by manufacturers of improved security against vandalism and theft.

Vending comes to heavy industry: a selection of snack and drink machines at a railway locomotive works in the 1960s.

At the 'Micro-Vend Buffet' in the staff restaurant (around 1970), food is selected from a cold cabinet for microwaving according to the instructions written very prominently above.

Into decimal coinage: smart new London Underground ticket machines.

DECIMALISATION AND ELECTRONICS

In the early 1970s the automatic vending industry was obliged to adjust to two major changes: decimalisation of the coinage and the introduction of value added tax.

In 1972 the Decimal Currency Board estimated that nearly twelve million coin-operated machines would need conversion, of which ten million were gas, electricity and television meters. Nearly a million machines were vending goods, including 300,000 cigarette machines, 220,000 confectionery machines and over 100,000 food and drink vending machines. Some 300,000 coin-operated machines were providing services such as issuing tickets, operating door locks, launderettes, parking meters, weighing machines and post office and telephone installations, while the rest were largely amusement and gaming machines.

Into decimal coinage: chocolate selling for 20p.

28

Into decimal coinage: 2p, 10p and 50p pieces only are accepted by this telephone, which has a minimum call charge of 6p.

The size and weight of coinage had been a significant factor in the manufacture and efficient working of the vending machine from its very inception. Fortunately, not all the coins changed on decimalisation so that not every piece of equipment required instant modification, but the heavy old copper coins disappeared, including the old penny – staple of the vending industry for so many years. And a new 50p piece was introduced, in the unfamiliar shape of an equilateral curved heptagon. Even more daunting to an inevitably price-conscious industry was that the cost of conversion fell upon the converter and, moreover, a vigorous government publicity campaign sought to ensure that conversion was as precise as possible from the old to the new price.

By this time more sophisticated machines were geared to accept a selection of coins, testing them for soundness, totalling them, returning an insufficient payment and giving change, but these were all the more likely to need adapting to new coins. For some of the older machines scrapping was to prove more economic than adaptation.

Out, for example, went the old penny weighing-machine, which lost its traditional coin and was already needing to convert its results from imperial to metric measure at a time when more serious weight-watchers were increasingly investing in domestic scales for the bathroom.

Scarcely had this change been dealt with

An electronic hot drinks display panel showing the range the customer can choose from.

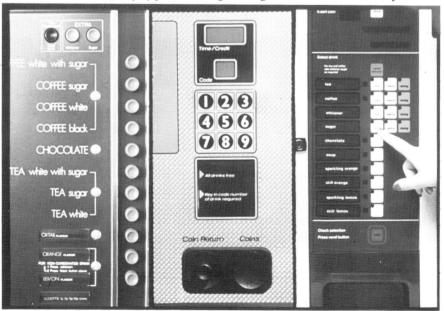

when the introduction of value added tax in 1973 caused prices to rise. Whilst the initial tax rate was relatively low, the prices of inexpensive items sold through automatic vending were hard to adjust without claims of unwarranted percentage increases.

Faced with these changes, forward-looking manufacturers sought to take early advantage of electronic technology, then in its infancy, by providing the additional features which the microprocessor could offer, and the new breed of vending machines became capable of providing a wider choice of goods and greater flexibility in their pricing.

The typical electronic automatic vending machine uses the computing power of the microprocessor to determine the sequence of operation of its electrical components. In addition, the electronic circuit contains memory devices to store the manufacturer's fixed instructions for allowing the machine to function and also the adjustable settings which enable the operator to vary the selections available and the prices to be charged. The memory devices may also include records of sales made and cash collected. Microprocessor control also enables the machine to identify faults so that the operator may more quickly restore empty or failed machines to full service.

Electronic checking of the validity of coins was also a boon to the operator. The use of dud coins and other 'slugs' to activate the system without payment had been a continuing problem. Pre-decimal coinage could become badly worn over years of use and a machine with controls set to reject slugs might also be found to reject worn legal tender, with consequent loss of genuine sales and customer goodwill. Decimal currency was, for the most part, newer and therefore more uniform. Nonetheless, whilst the old mechanical checks were retained, electronics enabled coins to be additionally checked by passing them through a magnetic field where the current led coins of false metal to pass through the system at different speeds from true coin and thus to be deflected into the reject channel of the machine. This combination of checks has made the acceptance of slugs a very rare occurrence and, indeed, the most modern systems can conduct even the older mechanical tests electronically.

The facility to add up combinations of inserted coins and to give change if necessary has also been enhanced by electronic controls. Once the customer has pressed the appropriate button to select the goods required, modern machines will display the amount needed to complete the sale, deliver the goods once the full

30

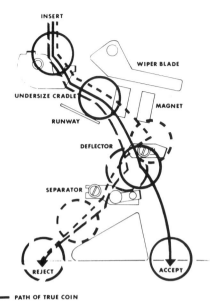

INSERT

WIPER BLADE

UNDERSIZE CRADLE

MAGNET

RUNWAY

DEFLECTOR

SEPARATOR

REJECT

ACCEPT

———— PATH OF TRUE COIN

— · — · PATH OF LEAD & GERMAN SILVER FAKES

— — PATH OF COPPER FAKES

The course of the coin: detecting fakes or 'slugs'.

section and capable of being replenished when necessary by diverting appropriate coins inserted by fresh customers.

Although electronics have also fostered the development of cash cards for automatic banking, pre-paid telephone cards for use in public telephones and other 'smart-card' alternatives to coin, coin-operated vending remains by far the most common method.

Meanwhile automatic vending machines are to be found more commonly in an increasing number of sites: in the 'budget' range of newer hotel chains, in leisure centres, hospitals, motorway service stations and other garage forecourts and in airport catering areas. Increasingly in these and other outlets a single multi-vending machine will be programmed to sell hot and cold drinks and snacks according to the customer's selection.

On vended snacks, drinks and confectionery the public is reckoned to spend £1 billion a year. Even leaving aside all other sales through automatic vending, this still demands a vast amount of coin to be put into – and emptied from – Britain's vending machines.

payment has been made and prevent further coin being inserted whilst delivery is completed. The machine will be programmed to give change where required, with a reservoir of change, each different denomination of coin stacked in its own

Vending at public baths in the 1980s. From the left: a change machine; one for 'soap, bath cubes etc'; one-price ticket machines for 'warm baths and showers', one for adults and one for juveniles; a towel machine; a food vender.

FURTHER READING

Colmer, Michael. *The Great Vending Machine Book.* Contemporary Books Inc (USA), 1977.

Rogers, John L. *Automatic Vending.* Food Trade Press, 1958.

Schreiber, G. Richard. *A Concise History of Vending in the United States.* National Automatic Vending Association (USA), 1990. Includes references to the early developments in the United Kingdom.

The Vending Book. Automatic Vending Association of Great Britain, 1987.

PLACES TO VISIT

Bristol Industrial Museum, Prince's Wharf, Prince Street, Bristol, Avon BS1 4RN. Telephone: 01179 251470. Automatic vending equipment not on public display: viewing by appointment only.

Museum of London, London Wall, London EC2Y 5HN. Telephone: 0171-600 3699.

London Transport Museum, Covent Garden, London WC2E 7BB. Telephone: 0171-379 6344.

National Railway Museum, Leeman Road, York YO2 4XJ. Telephone: 01904 621261.

York Castle Museum, York YO1 1RY. Telephone: 01904 653611.

This type of machine, selling Cadbury's chocolate and Wrigley's chewing gum, is often seen on station and underground platforms.